MY BABY BOOK

Illustrated by Anita Jeram

Based on

GUESS HOW MUCH I LOVE YOU

Written by Sam MᶜBratney

MY FAMILY

Before there was me…

"I spy something that belongs to me
and it's not my shadow."

WAITING FOR ME

Here is a scan of me before I was born.

My parents found out they were expecting me in the month of

_____

They felt _____

_____

The name of my mummy's doctor was _____

Mummy thought I would be a girl ☐   boy ☐

Daddy thought I would be a girl ☐   boy ☐

Here are some names they thought of for me if I was a girl:

_____

and if I was a boy: _____

_____

The name they finally chose for me was

_____

_____

because _____

_____

_____

Here is a picture of Mummy when she was expecting me.

While she was expecting me, Mummy loved these foods:

_____

She hated these foods: _____

My parents got ready for my arrival by _____

_____

_____

The date they first heard my heartbeat was _____

They felt _____

The date they first felt me kick was _____

It felt like _____

The due date was _____

Does nothing stay the same?
thought Little Nutbrown Hare.
Does everything change?

BEING BORN

At last – I arrived!

The date was _____ , so now that's my birthday!

The place was _____

When I was born it was day ☐   night ☐

The time was _____

Here is the first ever picture of me!

I weighed _____

I measured _____

The colour of my eyes was _____

_____

The colour of my hair was

_____

"It's little... It's nutbrown...
It's my most favourite thing...
And it can hop."

My parents said I looked like

_____

_____

_____

Other people said I looked like

_____

_____

_____

Guess who I think
I looked like…

"ME!"

FIRST DAYS

We travelled home from the hospital by _____

"We're here!
Home is my best place of all."

My first home was _____

On my first night at home, I slept _____

Here is a picture of my first house or room.

Some first presents I was given were

Here are messages from some of the first people I ever met.

SPECIAL THINGS
TO KEEP

Keep precious things like newspaper clippings,
name bracelets and birth announcements safe here.

MY FIRST FOOTPRINTS

"I love you
all the way up
to your toes!"

BATHTIME

My first bath was _____

My favourite bath toys were _____

_____

_____

_____

Here I am in the bath!

OTHER NEWS

*Across the river
and over the hills. . .*

Here are some clippings from newspapers and magazines.

The Prime Minister was

_____

Some other leaders
around the world were

_____

_____

_____

The clothes in style were _____

_____

_____

Some hit songs were

_____

_____

_____

Some famous film stars were

_____

_____

_____

Some famous sportspeople were

_____

_____

A newspaper cost _____ , a cinema ticket cost _____

and a pint of milk cost _____

A postage stamp looked like this:

SOME FIRST TIMES

I first slept through the night
when I was _____ old.

Big Nutbrown Hare settled Little Nutbrown Hare into his bed of leaves.
He leaned over and kissed him goodnight.

I first smiled when I was _____ old.

*Then Little Nutbrown Hare
began to smile and smile.*

I first discovered my hands when I was _____ old.

I first grasped something when I was _____ old.

I first discovered my feet when I was _____ old.

I first clapped when I was _____ old.

I first waved goodbye when I was _____ old.

MEALTIMES

My first tooth came in on _____

My second tooth came in on _____

My third tooth came in on _____

My fourth tooth came in on _____

The first solid food I ever tasted was _____

I first drank from a cup when I was _____ old.

I first used a spoon when I was _____ old.

I liked to eat _____

_____

_____

_____

I didn't like to eat _____

_____

_____

_____

… some of the plants that grew on Cloudy Mountain were very tasty.

UP AND ABOUT

I first held up my head when

I was _____ old.

I first rolled over when

I was _____ old.

I first sat up alone when I was _____ old.

I first crawled when I was _____ old.

I could pull myself up to standing
when I was _____ old.

I could stand alone when
I was _____ old.

At last! I took my first step
when I was _____ old.

That's good hopping, thought Little Nutbrown Hare.
I wish I could hop like that.

TALKING

My first word ever was _____

My first names for my parents were _____

_____

Some of my other first words were _____

_____

_____

_____

My favourite rhymes to say were _____

_____

My favourite songs to sing were _____

_____

_____

He wanted to be sure that
Big Nutbrown Hare was listening.

PLAYTIME

My first friends were

_____

_____

_____

_____

_____

I liked to play with

_____

_____

_____

_____

My favourite things to do
outside were _____

_____

_____

_____

_____

My favourite bedtime books were

_____

_____

_____

*They chased after
falling leaves until
Big Nutbrown Hare
could chase no more.*

PARTYTIME

The special days our family celebrated were _____

_____

The first special day we celebrated after I was born was _____

_____

Gifts I received that day were _____

_____

Some happy things that happened were _____

_____

_____

SOME MORE
FIRST TIMES

I first went swimming when I was _____ old.

I first went to the playground _____ *(date)*
when I was _____ old.

I wore my first pair of shoes _____ (date)

when I was _____ old.

They were _____

I had my first haircut when I was _____ old.

It was _____

envelope for lock of hair

LEARNING

Then Little Nutbrown Hare
had a good idea.

Here are some of my first experiments with a crayon.

BUMPS AND BRUISES

Some first illnesses I had were

_____

_____

_____

_____

_____

_____

My doctor's name was

_____

_____

Some baby medicines
I had to take were

_____

_____

Some illnesses I was
immunised against were

_____

_____

Some bumps and falls
I had were _____

_____

_____

_____

HOLIDAY TIME

The first holiday my family ever took with me was to _____

_____ when I was _____ old.

Some adventures we had were _____

_____

_____

_____

_____

"Oh, that's far," said Big Nutbrown Hare. "That is very, very far."

Here are some pictures of us on holiday.

GROWING

Here I am at three months old,

*"What does a little brown hare
like me turn into?"*
"A Big Nutbrown Hare – like me!"

six months old   and nine months old.

Now I am One!

People who sang "Happy Birthday" to me that day were

_____

Special birthday
things we ate were

Some gifts I was
given were

Here I am, exactly one year old!

NOW I AM TWO!

Here I am, exactly two years old!

Some gifts I was given that day were _____

_____

Songs we sang were _____

Games we played were _____

"Well, that certainly was an adventure!"

GETTING BIGGER

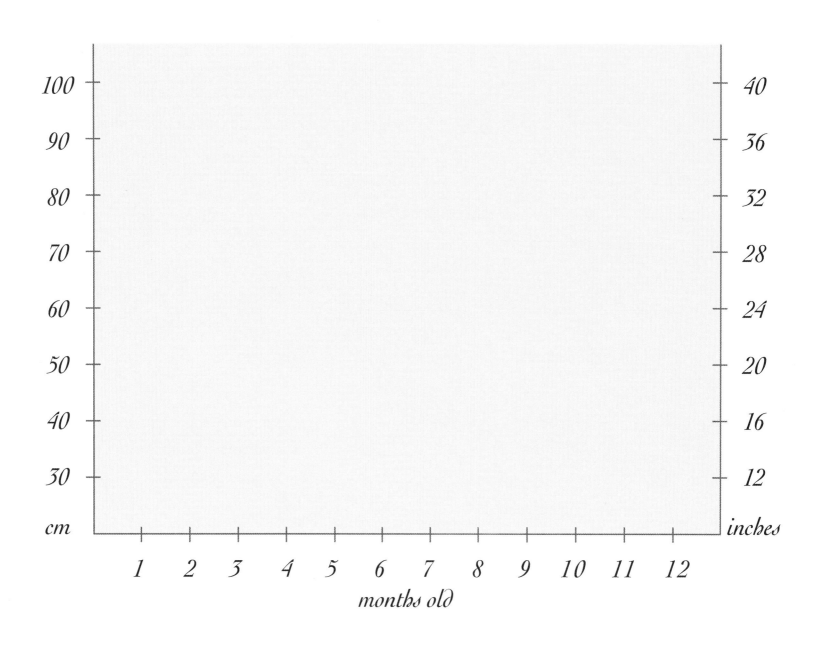

Big Nutbrown Hare was right there beside him.

SPECIAL MEMORIES

"And where you are," whispered Big Nutbrown Hare,
"is the best place in the whole world."